Twin to Twin

WRITTEN BY margaret o'hair ❋ ILLUSTRATED BY thierry courtin

Margaret K. McElderry Books New York London Toronto Sydney Singapore

Double born.
Twice the blessing.

Double kids.
Twice the messing.

Double babies'
blankies, binkies.

Double diapers,
clean or stinkies.

Double crawl,
then double walk.

Conversation,
double talk!

Double giggles
when they're glad.

Double tantrums
when they're mad.

Double love.
Double hugs.

Double catch
the lady bugs.

Double feed
the yellow ducks.

Double roll
toy cars and trucks.

Double ride
the shaggy pony.

Double cheese
and macaroni!

Double kites
on a string.

High and low
on the swing.

Double singing
where they go—

"Eee aye eee aye eee aye oh!"

Double rolling
down the hill.

Double Band-Aids
when they spill.

Double shirts.
Double jeans.

Belly buttons
in between.

Double splashing
in the tub.

Double bubbles.
Double scrub.

Double brushing
shiny teeth.

Double monster.
Check underneath!

Double dance.
Double smile.

Double jump.
Pillow pile!

Mirror double.
Peek and see.

Am I you?
Or are you me?

Double hold
their teddy bears.

Double kisses,
hugs, and prayers.

Double tired
from all their play.

Double dreams
for their next day.

Double hands,
skin to skin.

Double hearts,
twin to twin.